Charles M. Schulz

SNOOPY
and
THE PEANUTS GANG

STAY COOL

ℛℛ

Ravette London

Printed and bound for Ravette Limited,
3 Glenside Estate, Star Road,
Partridge Green, Horsham,
Sussex RH13 8RA
by Mateu Cromo Artes Gráfica, s.a.

ISBN: 1 85304 012 6

RATS! THERE GOES THE BELL..

I CAN'T STAND IT!

OH, HOW I HATE THESE LUNCH HOURS!

I ALWAYS HAVE TO EAT ALONE BECAUSE NOBODY LIKES ME..

PEANUT BUTTER AGAIN..

I WISH THAT LITTLE RED-HAIRED GIRL WOULD COME OVER, AND SIT WITH ME...

WOULDN'T IT BE GREAT IF SHE'D WALK OVER HERE, AND SAY," MAY I EAT LUNCH WITH YOU, CHARLIE BROWN?"

I'D GIVE ANYTHING TO TALK WITH HER...SHE'D NEVER LIKE ME, THOUGH...I'M SO BLAH AND SO STUPID... SHE'D NEVER LIKE ME...

I WONDER WHAT WOULD HAPPEN IF I WENT OVER AND TRIED TO TALK TO HER! EVERY-BODY WOULD PROBABLY LAUGH. SHE'D PROBABLY BE INSULTED, TOO, IF SOMEONE AS BLAH AS I AM TRIED TO TALK TO HER

1-20

I HATE LUNCH HOUR...ALL IT DOES IS MAKE ME LONELY...DURING CLASS IT DOESN'T MATTER....

I CAN'T EVEN EAT... NOTHING TASTES GOOD...

WHY CAN'T I EAT LUNCH WITH THAT LITTLE RED-HAIRED GIRL? THEN I'D BE HAPPY...

RATS! NOBODY IS EVER GOING TO LIKE ME..

LUNCH HOUR IS THE LONELIEST HOUR OF THE DAY'!

PEANUTS by SCHULZ

WHAT'S THIS?

OH, IT'S JUST A LITTLE PICTURE I DREW OF A MAN ON A HORSE...

OH, I JUST LOVE HORSE PICTURES!

COULD I HAVE IT, CHARLIE BROWN? COULD I HAVE IT TO HANG ON MY WALL?

WELL, I GUESS SO... IF YOU THINK IT'S GOOD ENOUGH...I MEAN..

AND HOW ABOUT SIGNING IT? WILL YOU SIGN IT, TOO? WILL YOU PUT YOUR NAME ON IT?

ALL RIGHT..WHAT DO YOU WANT ME TO DO...JUST SIGN MY NAME, OR...

YOU WERE GOING TO DO IT, WEREN'T YOU?

HA!HA!HA!HA! HA!HA!HA!HA!

YOU REALLY THOUGHT I WANTED TO HANG THIS STUPID PICTURE ON MY WALL, DIDN'T YOU? HA!HA!HA!HA!

..AND HE EVEN THOUGHT I WANTED HIM TO SIGN IT! HA!HA!HA!HA!

I CAN'T STAND IT!

COME BACK HERE, YOU COWARD!

YOU LITTLE SNEAK!

DON'T THINK YOU CAN GET AWAY FROM ME FOREVER! I'M GONNA KNOCK YOUR BLOCK OFF!

I'M GONNA MANGLE YOU! I'M GONNA ANNIHILATE YOU!

2-17

YOU'RE IN THIS TOO, SNOOPY! IF YOU PROTECT HIM, I'LL GIVE YOU JUST WHAT I'M GONNA GIVE HIM!!

IT'S NOT FAIR!

YOU PROMISED ME A PARTY! IT'S NOT FAIR! IT'S NOT FAIR!

YOU PROMISED ME A BIRTHDAY PARTY, AND NOW YOU SAY I CAN'T HAVE ONE! IT'S NOT FAIR!

YOU'RE NOT USING THE RIGHT STRATEGY

WHAT?

THE MORE YOU FUSS, THE WORSE OFF YOU'LL BE...WHY NOT ADMIT IT WAS ALL YOUR OWN FAULT?

WHY NOT GO UP TO MOM, AND SAY TO HER, "I'M SORRY, DEAR MOTHER...I ADMIT I'VE BEEN BAD, AND YOU WERE RIGHT TO CANCEL MY PARTY...FROM NOW ON, I SHALL TRY TO BE GOOD"

THAT'S MUCH BETTER THAN RANTING AND RAVING...ALL THAT DOES IS PROVE HER POINT

"I'M SORRY, DEAR MOTHER, I ADMIT I'VE BEEN BAD, AND YOU WERE RIGHT TO CANCEL MY PARTY... FROM NOW ON, I SHALL TRY TO BE GOOD!"

I'D RATHER DIE!

SLURP
SLUP
SLURP

WHERE? RIGHT HERE, THAT'S WHERE!
RIGHT HERE ON PAGE THIRTY-ONE,
SECTION THREE, RULE 6.12!

I LOVE A GOOD RHUBARB

5-12

HOLD STILL!

HOLD STILL, I SAY!

IS THIS A SCHOOL PROJECT, LUCY?

OF COURSE, IT IS, YOU BLOCK-HEAD! WHY ELSE WOULD I BE CHASING A BUNCH OF STUPID BUTTERFLIES?!

HERE... I THINK MAYBE YOUR TEACHER WILL LIKE THESE..

PROMISE YOU'LL LET THEM GO AFTER YOU'VE STUDIED THEM, WILL YOU?

I JUST CAN'T BELIEVE THAT RACHEL CARSON WOULD EVER LET HERSELF GET SO UPSET!

BEETHOVEN... HA!

EVERYONE TALKS ABOUT HOW GREAT BEETHOVEN WAS...

7-28

BEETHOVEN WASN'T SO GREAT!

WHAT DO YOU MEAN, BEETHOVEN WASN'T SO GREAT?

HE NEVER GOT HIS PICTURE ON BUBBLE GUM CARDS, DID HE?

HAVE YOU EVER SEEN HIS PICTURE ON BUBBLE GUM CARDS? HUH?

HOW CAN YOU SAY SOMEONE IS GREAT WHO'S NEVER HAD HIS PICTURE ON BUBBLE GUM CARDS?

THAT'S WHAT I MEAN WHEN I SAY BEETHOVEN WASN'T SO GREAT!

THIS HAS BEEN A GOOD DAY!

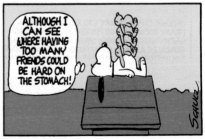

WHAT'S HE DOING SITTING OVER THERE?

HEY, SCHROEDER! AREN'T YOU GONNA PLAY?

I CAN'T...I'M JUST GETTING OVER THE CHICKEN POX!

MOM SAID I COULD WATCH YOU GUYS PLAY, BUT NOT TO GO NEAR ANYONE... IT'S CATCHING...

C'MON, CHARLIE BROWN... PUT IT OVER!

8-25

POW!

Tm. Reg. U. S. Pat Off.—All rights reserved
Copr. 1963 by United Feature Syndicate, Inc.

JUST WHAT I NEED...A HANDFUL OF CHICKEN POX!

PEANUTS by SCHULZ

STUPID LEAVES!

9-29

Tm. Reg. U. S. Pat. Off.—All rights reserved
Copr. 1963 by United Feature Syndicate, Inc.

GOLLY! HAVE YOU EVER SEEN SO MANY SNAKES AND LIZARDS IN ALL YOUR LIFE?!! NO...AND SPIDERS, TOO... SPIDERS, TOO? YEAH, SNAKES AND LIZARDS AND SPIDERS!

AND THEY'RE ALL HEADED THIS WAY, YOU SAY? YEAH, THERE'S A WHOLE FLOCK OF 'EM...ALL HEADED THIS WAY...CREEPING AND CRAWLING...SNAKES AN' LIZARDS AN'...

HEY! YOU WANT A PIECE OF CANDY?

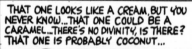

CHOCOLATES, EH? HOW NICE...LET'S SEE NOW...I MUST MAKE SURE I DON'T GET ONE WITH COCONUT IN IT...I CAN'T STAND COCONUT...LET'S SEE NOW...HMM...

THAT ONE LOOKS LIKE A CREAM, BUT YOU NEVER KNOW...THAT ONE COULD BE A CARAMEL...THERE'S NO DIVINITY, IS THERE? THAT ONE IS PROBABLY COCONUT...

THE LIGHT COLORED ONES ARE USUALLY GOOD ALTHOUGH THE DARK COLORED ONES ARE SOMETIMES CREAMS...I DON'T KNOW ABOUT THOSE SQUARE ONES...I WONDER IF...

TAKE ONE

COCONUT!

12-8   SCHULZ

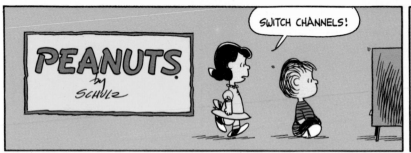

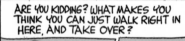

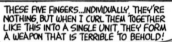

OKAY, SWITCH CHANNELS!

OH, NO! NOT AGAIN!

I NEVER GET TO WATCH WHAT I WANT TO WATCH!

NEVER! NEVER! NEVER! NEVER!

1-12

Tm. Reg. U. S. Pat Off.—All rights reserved
Copr. 1964 by United Feature Syndicate, Inc.

I HOPE YOUR PROGRAM GETS A LOUSY RATING!

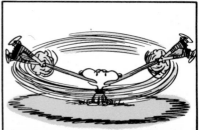

BOY, WAS IT COLD LAST NIGHT!

2-23

FROZEN WATER-DISH!

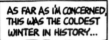

PEANUTS by SCHULZ

OH, NO!

THAT BLOCKHEAD!

DID YOU TEAR THE COVER OFF THIS COMIC MAGAZINE?

YES, I GUESS I DID...

3-15

BUT WHY? WHY DO YOU DO SUCH STUPID THINGS?

I DON'T KNOW...I REALLY DON'T KNOW..

I'VE ASKED MYSELF THAT, TOO...I'VE ASKED MYSELF THAT VERY QUESTION..

WHY DO I DO STUPID THINGS? WHY DON'T I THINK? WHAT'S THE MATTER WITH ME? WHERE'S MY SENSE OF RESPONSIBILITY?

THEN I ASK MYSELF, AM I REALLY RESPONSIBLE? IS IT REALLY MY FAULT WHEN I DO SOMETHING WRONG? MUST I ANSWER FOR MY MISTAKES?

WHO IS RESPONSIBLE? WHO IS ACCOUNTABLE? WHO IS...

POW!

HER KIND NEVER WORRIES ABOUT THESE THINGS!

SCHULZ

OUR MANAGER

HERE..HAVE A DOUGHNUT..

THANK YOU..

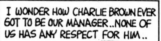

I WONDER HOW CHARLIE BROWN EVER GOT TO BE OUR MANAGER..NONE OF US HAS ANY RESPECT FOR HIM..

MANAGER

I SUPPOSE IT'S A MATTER OF DEDICATION..

CHARLIE BROWN IS THE ONLY ONE WHO IS COMPLETELY DEDICATED TO BASEBALL..THIS IS WHAT MAKES A GOOD MANAGER..

3-29

I THINK HE'D RATHER MANAGE THAN EAT

HERE, CHARLIE BROWN.. HAVE A DOUGHNUT..

NO, THANK YOU.. I'D RATHER MANAGE!

MANAGER

YOU'RE RIGHT!

HAVE YOU EVER DONE ANY SOAP CARVING?

SOAP CARVING?

YES, IT'S GREAT!

I'VE BEEN WORKING ON THIS MODEL OF AN OLD SAILING VESSEL

I WANT YOU TO SEE IT, CHARLIE BROWN...I CARVED IT ALL BY MYSELF..

I'M ESPECIALLY PROUD OF THE GOOD JOB I DID ON THE SAILS...IT TOOK ME THREE DAYS TO DO JUST THE SAILS ALONE..

4-5

IF YOU'RE GOING TO GET YOUR HANDS REALLY CLEAN, YOU'VE GOT TO WORK UP A GOOD LATHER

LOTS OF SOAP AND HOT WATER..THAT'S WHAT DOES IT!

Tm. Reg. U. S. Pat Off.—All rights reserved
Copr. 1964 by United Feature Syndicate, Inc.

I HAD PLANNED TO SHOW YOU AN AUTHENTIC REPLICA OF AN AMERICAN CLIPPER SHIP.. WOULD YOU SETTLE FOR A CANOE?

ARE YOU GOING TO BUY COMIC BOOKS, CHARLIE BROWN?

NOT ON YOUR LIFE!

4-12

SEE THIS FIVE DOLLARS? I'M GOING TO SPEND IT ALL ON BUBBLE GUM CARDS! I'VE **GOT** TO GET A PICTURE OF **JOE SHLABOTNIK!**

FIVE DOLLARS' WORTH OF BUBBLE GUM, PLEASE!

I'D DO ANYTHING TO GET A JOE SHLABOTNIK BUBBLE GUM CARD.. HE'S MY HERO...

FIVE DOLLARS' WORTH OF BUBBLE GUM, AND NOT ONE JOE SHLABOTNIK!

A PENNY'S WORTH OF BUBBLE GUM, PLEASE..

Tm. Reg. U. S. Pat. Off.—All rights reserved
Copr. 1964 by United Feature Syndicate, Inc.

WELL, WHAT DO YOU KNOW....JOE SHLABOTNIK!

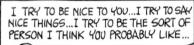

PEANUTS by SCHULZ

WILLIE MAYS ALVIN DARK SNOOPY ORLANDO CEPEDA

4-26

IT'S A LIVING!

HAPPY MOTHER'S DAY!

FROM YOUR SON (Me)

LISTEN TO THIS...

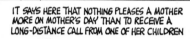

IT SAYS HERE THAT NOTHING PLEASES A MOTHER MORE ON MOTHER'S DAY THAN TO RECEIVE A LONG-DISTANCE CALL FROM ONE OF HER CHILDREN

5-10

THAT'S A GOOD THOUGHT...

HELLO..... MOM?

SCHULZ

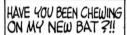

PEANUTS by SCHULZ

CLOMP! AUA!

7-19

CALL THE HUMANE SOCIETY FOR ME, AND ASK THEM HOW LONG I'D HAVE TO STAY IN JAIL IF I PUNCHED A BEAGLE IN THE NOSE...

PEANUTS by SCHULZ

THEY'RE IN THE TREE AGAIN..

BY THIS TIME YOU'D THINK THEY'D KNOW BETTER!

MOM SAYS FOR YOU GUYS TO GET DOWN FROM THAT TREE RIGHT NOW!

8-23

STUPID KIDS!

SHE SAYS, "WHAT ARE YOU TRYING TO DO...BREAK YOUR NECKS?"

THAT MEANS YOU, TOO!

OH, NO!

THANK YOU..

8-30

THE RAIN STOPPED, CHARLIE BROWN...WHAT DID YOU DO, CALL THE WEATHERMAN?

NO, "DIAL-A-PRAYER"!

PEANUTS by SCHULZ

SAY! I LIKE THAT CAP, LUCY! THANK YOU..

YOU'RE ALL SET FOR COLD WEATHER, AREN'T YOU? YES, I GUESS I AM..

YOU KNOW WHAT IT'S LIKE TO BE COLD AND UNCOMFORTABLE, DON'T YOU? OH, YES... I KNOW THAT FEELING...

YOU LIKE ANIMALS, DON'T YOU? I MEAN, YOU'VE ALWAYS BEEN SORT OF AN ANIMAL LOVER, HAVEN'T YOU? OF COURSE!

DOGS, TOO? ESPECIALLY DOGS WHO SLEEP OUTSIDE, AND SHIVER AND SHAKE ALL NIGHT? *SIGH*

11-15

Happiness is catching snowflakes on your tongue.

12-18

Happiness is a Christmas vacation with no book reports to write.

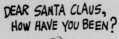
DEAR SANTA CLAUS, HOW HAVE YOU BEEN?

PLEASE DON'T GET THE IDEA THAT I AM WRITING BECAUSE I WANT SOMETHING.

NOTHING COULD BE FURTHER FROM THE TRUTH. I WANT NOTHING.

IF YOU WANT TO SKIP OUR HOUSE THIS YEAR, GO RIGHT AHEAD. I WON'T BE OFFENDED. REALLY I WON'T.

SPEND YOUR TIME ELSEWHERE. DON'T BOTHER WITH ME. I REALLY MEAN IT.

WHAT IN THE WORLD KIND OF LETTER IS THIS?!!

I'M HOPING THAT HE'LL FIND MY ATTITUDE PECULIARLY REFRESHING

12-20

SCHULZ